EASY RECORDER TUNES

Written and designed by
Philip Hawthorn
Edited by Jenny Tyler

Illustrated by Kim Blundell
Original music by Philip Hawthorn
Consultant: Stephanie Roberts

Music engraving: Poco Ltd., Letchworth, Herts

SCHOLASTIC INC.

New York Toronto London Auckland Sydney
Mexico City New Delhi Hong Kong Buenos Aires

Contents

About this book

This book has lots of tunes which you can play on your soprano recorder. It will also help you to read and understand music better, and improve your skill as a recorder player.

In this book there are folk songs from all over the world, jazz tunes and tunes from classical music. Other tunes have been specially written. There are also tunes for two players.

At the beginning, the tunes only use a few different notes. They use more as you go through the book. There are diagrams to help you get the right fingering for each note.

On many pages you can find out about music symbols and words. When you see an asterisk in the music, it tells you that there is something explained in a box at the bottom of the page.

The recorder comes from a very old family of instruments. You can find out about the different members of the family, as well as the ancestors of your modern soprano recorder.

There are a lot of interesting facts about many of the tunes in the book. You can also find out about some of the composers who wrote the music, such as Mozart and Beethoven.

Playing notes

Below are some fingering diagrams. These remind you which fingers to use to play the notes. They also show where the notes are written on the staff. Whenever there is a new note in a tune, there will be a fingering diagram for it.

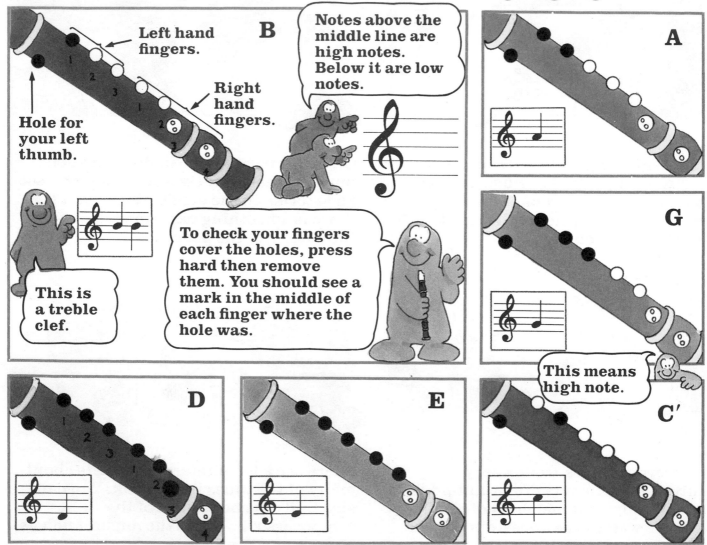

Your index finger is 1, middle finger is 2, and so on.

Sloppy Joe

Note lengths

Notes lengths are measured in beats. Below is a chart with three note lengths in it.

Quarter note

1 beat

Half note

2 beats

Whole note

4 beats

Using your tongue to blow notes

Before you blow a note, put your tongue behind your top teeth. Now move your tongue as if you were saying "tah" as you blow into the recorder.

Hold the note for the correct number of beats.

To finish the note, put your tongue back behind your teeth as you stop blowing.

This is called tonguing. It gives notes a crisp start and finish.

Don't blow too hard or you may get a squeak.

Bars and time signatures

Music is divided up into bars. Each bar has the same number of beats in it. The numbers at the beginning of the music are called the time signature. This tells you how many beats in a bar, and how long those beats are.

This four means there are four beats in each bar...

this one says they are quarter note length.

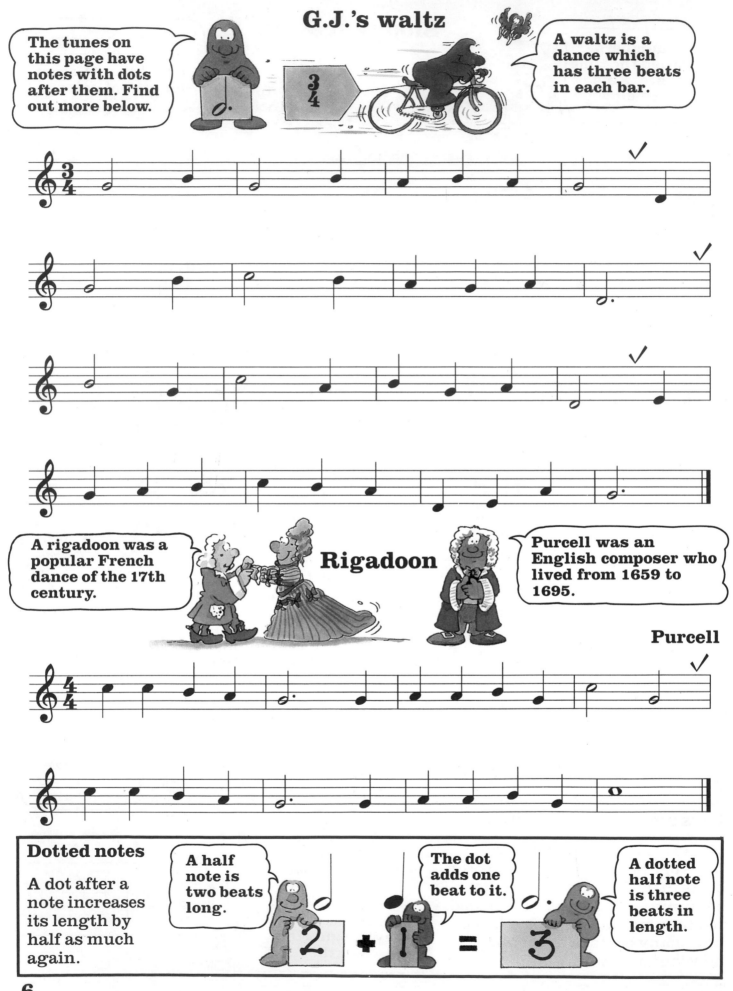

Aiken drum

The tune below starts with an incomplete bar, called a part bar. Find out more below.

This tune is from an English folk song.

English

Sore feet

Play this tune quite slowly at first as it has a lot of eighth notes in it.

Part bars

When a tune starts with a part bar, count the beats that are "missing" in your head before you play. This will help you to get the rhythm right.

1, 2, 3, 4

A part bar is also called an anacrusis.

In the top tune above, count three beats before you play the eighth notes.

The last bar has the "missing" beats from the anacrusis.

8

Lavender's blue

There's a hole in my bucket

Sharp notes

Sometimes, two notes with letter names that are next to each other have a note in between them. This is called a sharp note, or "sharp" for short.*

* *Sometimes the note is called a "flat". Find out more on page 34.*

O come all ye faithful

English

Playing loudly and softly

The letters in music which tell you how loudly or softly to play stand for Italian words. This is because the way music is written today is based on the ideas of an Italian monk called Guido d'Arezzo who lived from 995 to 1050.

Soft words

These words are based on the Italian word *piano* which means soft.

Loud words

These words are based on the Italian word *forte* (for-tay), meaning loud.

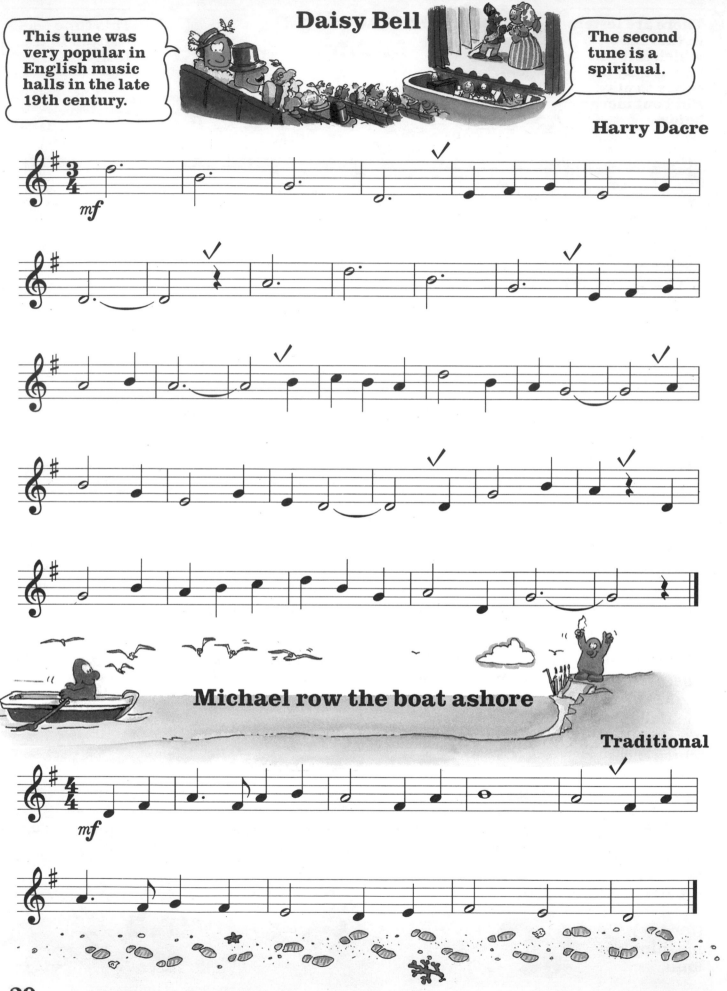

Funky tortoise (Part B)

Tunes for two players

Tunes for two people are called duets. You could play "Funky Tortoise" with a friend. One of you plays part A and the other part B.

D.C. al Fine

You play the repeats as normal. When you get to the end of the tune, you go back to the start and play until you get to the word *Fine*.

Playing high E

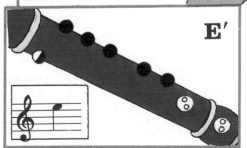

23

Roller skater rag

Ash grove

Welsh

Heads, shoulders, knees and toes

This tune is from an English folk song called "There is a tavern in the town".

It has a low F natural in it. You can find out about it below.

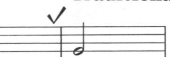

Traditional

The end of this tune sounds like something being dropped from a great height.

Butterfingers

pp ———————————————————— *ff*

Remembering *cres* and *dim*

The picture below shows you an easy way of remembering which symbol is which.

The words *cres* and *dim* are sometimes used instead of symbols.

The wider the gap between the lines, the louder you play.

The narrower the gap, the softer you play.

cres
dim

Playing low F natural

F natural is quite tricky. Practice by playing it before and after other notes you can play.

F

Recorder disorder

On these two pages you can find out some interesting recorder facts.

Spooky boogie

The oldest recorder
The oldest recorder in the world was made some time before 1400. It was found under a 15th century stone house in Dortrecht, which is in the Netherlands.

It is about the same size as a modern soprano recorder.

It is made in one piece rather than two or three, like recorders today.

The recorder is now in the Gemeentemuseum in The Hague, Netherlands.

The wood it is made of is elm.

Patapan

There is a note in this tune called B flat. It has this sign. Find out more below.

French

Briskly
mf

Moderato means moderately fast. About the same as andante.

Auld lang syne

This tune is sung on New Year's Eve in many countries.

Scottish

Moderato
mf

f

Playing flats

Flats are named after notes they are next to, like sharps. A flat is called after the note it is below.

This note is B♭.

It is sometimes called A♯.

Here is a good way to remember which is which: flats go down, like flat tires.

B♭/A♯

Ecossaise

This tune was a very popular dance. The title is French for "Scottish".

Beethoven was born in Germany in 1770. He went deaf in about 1812, but went on writing music right up to his death in 1827.

Beethoven

From "Pastoral" Symphony

This tune is from music written to make you think of country scenes.

It is from Beethoven's Sixth Symphony.

Beethoven

37

Scarborough fair

This is an old English folk song. Scarborough is a town in Yorkshire, England.

English

Morning has broken

This tune was originally a folk song.

It later became a hymn.

English

38

Kum by ya

Oranges and lemons

Wedding march

Wagner was a German composer who lived from 1813 to 1883. This tune is from his opera* called "Lohengrin".

It is often played at weddings, as the bride enters the church.

Wagner

This tune has a G# in it. Find out about it on the opposite page.

Aria

An aria is the name given to a solo song in an opera.

* An opera is a kind of play in which all the words are sung.

The first Noel

This tune is used for Away in a Manger in Britain.

From "Adagio"

Tommaso Albinoni was an Italian composer who lived from 1671 to 1751.

Adagio means "slowly". There are more symbols explained below.

Albinoni

Triplets

Three eighth notes with a "3" over them are triplets. You play them in the space of just one beat. Clap the rhythm below as you say the words.

I like — 1 beat
Tedd-ing-ton — 1 beat

Triplets are a little faster than eighths.

This note and two symbols are in the tunes opposite.

Trills

With a trill, you play the note and the one above it very quickly for the length of the note.

Accents

This sign is an accent. Tongue the note with extra force to make it stand out from the others.

For example, when you see this..

..You play this very fast.

A′

Ledger line.

Baroque recorders

Baroque recorders were similar to the shape of modern recorders. Many had very beautiful and extravagant decorations.

This one is made from ivory.

It was carved in 1704. The baroque period was known for its ornate music and building designs.

Helston furry dance

This tune is also known as the "Floral Dance". It is danced every year on May 8th.

Helston is in Cornwall, England.

English

Greensleeves

This tune was written in the 16th century.

English

This tune was very popular in the late 19th century.

Grandfather's clock

Henry Clay Work

Andante

This is a traditional dance tune.

English country garden

English

Lightly

47

50

Botany Bay

This folk song was written by the first settlers in Australia. Many of them first arrived at Botany Bay.

Botany Bay is near the city of Sydney.

Australian

With a swing

57

59

Shakers' tune

On these two pages, the top staff is for the recorder. The bottom two are for a piano or electronic keyboard.

The bottom two staffs are called the accompaniment.*

American

60 * You could also play the tune without the accompaniment.

Lullaby

* A grace note is like an acciaccatura - play it before the main beat.

Music help

On this page you can see the music words and symbols that are used in this book. The index on the next page will tell you the page on which they are explained.

Speeds

presto	very fast	*andante*	fairly fast	*moderato*	moderately
allegro	fast	*adagio*	fairly slow	*cantabile*	in a flowing style
allegretto	not too fast	*lento*	slow	*ritardando*	slowing down

Symbols

repeat marks		grace notes		moderately loud	*mf*
dotted		triplets		moderately soft	*mp*
breath mark		emphasis		softly	*p*
tie		accent		very softly	*pp*
pause		tr	*tr*	crescendo	
staccato		very loudly	*ff*	*diminuendo*	
slur		loudly	*f*		

Scales and key signatures

A scale is a series of eight notes from one note to the next one with the same letter name. Below is the scale of C major. The key signature is also called C major. It tells you which sharps and flats are in the scale.

Here are the names of other key signatures in the book.

G major
D major
F major
Bb major

Fingering chart

Here is a chart which shows you the fingerings for all the notes in the book.

It also tells you on which page the note is explained.

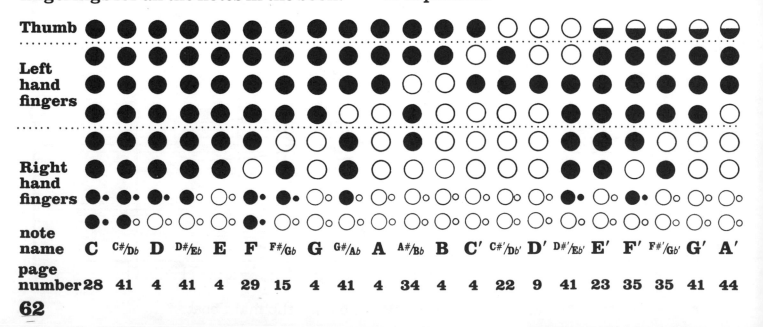

	Thumb	Left hand fingers			Right hand fingers			

note name	C	C#/Db	D	D#/Eb	E	F	F#/Gb	G	G#/Ab	A	A#/Bb	B	C'	C#'/Db'	D'	D#'/Eb'	E'	F'	F#'/Gb'	G'	A'
page number	28	41	4	41	4	29	15	4	41	4	34	4	4	22	9	41	23	35	35	41	44

On this page there is some information about your recorder.

There are also some helpful hints for practicing music.

The soprano recorder

Below you can find out what all the different parts of the recorder are called.

The one in the picture has three joints, but some recorders have two.

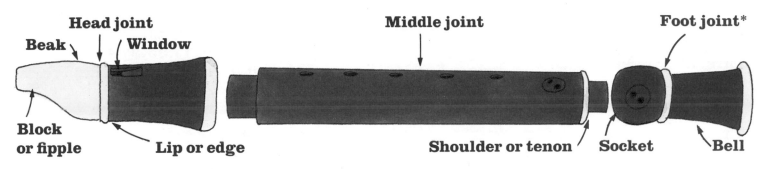

Head joint

Beak **Window**

Middle joint

Foot joint*

Block or fipple

Lip or edge

Shoulder or tenon **Socket** **Bell**

Different recorders

On the right are the five most common recorders. The smallest, the sopranino, is about 9½in long. The bass recorder is about 35in long.

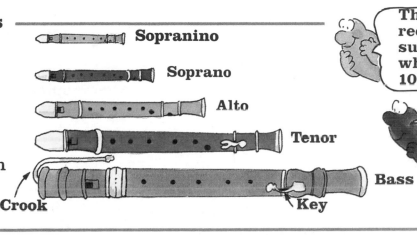

Sopranino

Soprano

Alto

Tenor

Crook **Key**

Bass

The largest recorder is a sub-contra bass, which is about 10 feet long.

The smallest is the Garklein recorder, which is only 4½in long.

Practicing music

Before you play the tune...

When you play the tune..

Check the key signature so you know what sharps or flats to play.

Play through at a speed you can manage, even if you make a few mistakes.

Read through the music to check for music instructions and letters.

Play the sections you found difficult until you get them right. Play slowly at first, then get faster.

 Tap out the rhythm of any difficult passages of the music.

 Work at the tune until you can play confidently, without mistakes.

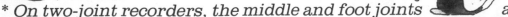
* *On two-joint recorders, the middle and foot joints*  *are one piece.*

Index

ISBN 0-439-32761-X

14 15 16 17 18 19 20   6/0

Printed in the U.S.A.   14

First Scholastic printing, September 2001